Mark and Michelle
on holiday

MARCEL MARLIER

ap
award publications

"Are you trying to stand on your head, Michelle?" asked Mark.

"I'm looking at reflections in the water," said Michelle. "Like this, they look the right way up."

Mark and Michelle were on holiday in the South of France. A wide river ran near the house where they were staying, and the children were allowed to use a small red canoe. They could both swim, and their mother had made them promise to be very careful.

One day they had gone with their mother and father to find the source of the river – a little spring which grew into a brook. Then it cascaded over rocks in a rushing waterfall. At last, in the valley, it turned into the slow-moving river near their holiday house.

"I love water," said Michelle. "So much happens near it, doesn't it?"

"Yes," said Mark, "and wasn't it wonderful when we went to the great Verdon gorge yesterday, and Daddy told us that

for millions of years the water had slowly cut through the rock
till it now runs at the bottom of steep cliffs."

"I was a bit scared when we stood at the top of the gorge and
looked down!" said Michelle.

Next day Mark and Michelle scrambled up a waterfall.
"You'd think the birds would be afraid of the noise of the water,"
said Michelle, "but look! That dipper is actually nesting under the
waterfall."

dippers at their nest

A wagtail flew down, perched on a nearby rock and bobbed its tail up and down. The bird is so slender and graceful that in Italy it is called the "ballerina".

The children crouched down to watch it. "It must be hard for birds to find anything to eat in all this rushing water," said Michelle.

"I looked that up in a book before we came," said Mark. "They eat freshwater crayfish, insect larvae and fish eggs."

a wagtail and nestlings

"Fish eggs?" asked Michelle. "Surely fish can't live in a waterfall like this, can they?"

"Trout love this kind of water, and so do some shell fish, such as fresh water lobster. You see those odd bits of rock and shells stuck together?

That's the covering a caddis worm makes to protect itself before it turns into a caddis fly."

caddis fly larvae in protective covering

One day they paddled their canoe
along the river and found
an old water mill.
"There's a grey wagtail,"
said Michelle, "with a black
bib. I expect it's nesting
in the stonework
round the wheel."

MARLIER

They paddled on down a quiet
stretch of water between tall
trees. It was rather dark
and shadowy.
"I hope we aren't lost," said
Michelle anxiously. "Look, some sea-gulls!
Does that mean we are nearly down to the sea?"
"Don't be a goose!" said Mark. "Those
are black-headed gulls, and they come a long
way up river in search of food.
They eat worms and snails
and insects. And don't worry,
we aren't lost. We'll
turn back soon,
and paddle upstream."

grey wagtail

black-headed gull

They landed, and very
quietly climbed a tree
to look down on the nest of a crested
grebe. It was a floating raft made of
water plants fastened together with reeds.

They paddled among some water lilies, and saw a water-boatman zigzagging about.

"And there's a dragonfly," said Mark, "and two more dragonflies on that water lily leaf. The female is going to lay her eggs, and the male is holding her, ready to carry her off if there's any danger. I can see a whirligig beetle, too."

"The dragonfly's eggs hatch out under water into very ugly creatures called nymphs," said Mark. "They have a curious lower lip, which they whip out to catch their prey. They are very fierce! After two years the nymph climbs up a stalk out of the water, its skin cracks and out comes the beautiful dragonfly to dry itself in the sun."

"It's odd that such a lovely thing should be so fierce in the early stages of its life," said Michelle.

"No fiercer than the water beetle," said Mark. "That has strong jaws and attacks everything – even frogs."

They paddled quietly past a fisherman.

On facing page:

1   *dragonfly nymph*

2 & 3 *dragonflies
         shedding their skin*

4   *larva of water
         beetle*

5   *water beetle*

6   *boat-fly, which can
         swim on its back*

7   *water bug*

Mark was daydreaming that he was swimming under water among the fish, when suddenly Michelle called to him to look at two kingfishers. One of them plunged into the water and came back with a fish in its beak.

1 speckled trout; 2 carp; 3 golden perch; 4 pike

The children paddled towards the river bank to have a close look at some herons. One stood in the water, a long leg folded beneath it. Suddenly it plunged its beak into the water, threw a fish into the air, caught it again – and swallowed it.

Herons are graceful birds, with slow, elegant movements – until that quick flash when they catch a fish. But the children remembered a more beautiful bird they had once seen in an orchard overlooking an old French town. This was a bee-eater, a bird with such brightly coloured plumage that in France it is sometimes called the rainbow bird.

Suddenly they saw an otter standing up on the bank. They could see her long whiskers, webbed feet and thick tail. She frisked in and out of holes and over fallen trees as if she were playing a game. Then she slithered down a steep slope into the river. They watched her twisting and turning under the water.

"I wish we could have an otter as a pet," said Mark. "They are very easy to train."

"Wouldn't it be fun!" said Michelle. "But the house would get very wet with an otter in it!"

Then Mark and Michelle had a wonderful piece of luck. Hanging from a tree they saw a birds' nest with a funnel shaped entrance. One bird was perched on the nest; another bird flew nearby. When they got home they looked the birds up in a book and found they were a rare kind of tit which builds these unusual nests. What a find!